WE WON'T LE
THEM
KEEP US THERE
A CATS PLACE
IS
EVERYWHERE
PRUDIE
WOZ 'ERE

To Sam

Love

Robert + Christopher

PRUDIE FINDS OUT

WRITTEN AND ILLUSTRATED BY NATANIA AND LITZA JANSZ

£3.50

PANDORA PRESS

Routledge & Kegan Paul
London, Boston, Melbourne and Henley

To Peggy and Cliff

First published in 1983
by Pandora Press
(Routledge & Kegan Paul plc)
39 Store Street, London WC1E 7DD,
9 Park Street, Boston, Mass. 02108, USA,
296 Beaconsfield Parade, Middle Park,
Melbourne, 3206, Australia, and
Broadway House, Newtown Road,
Henley-on-Thames, Oxon RG9 1EN
Set in 'Monophoto' Gill Sans 262
Filmset and Printed by BAS Printers Limited,
Over Wallop, Hampshire

ISBN 0 86358 003 3

Part I Prudie Finds Out

Prudie Pratt, an average cat,
Lived in a cosy council flat
And as she rarely came or went
The best part of her life was spent
In overlooking Peckham Rye,
Where trains and youth
both passed her by.

But life was simple as a pet
Observing Household Etiquette
Which she learnt at an early age
The Rules are on the other page:

‘Don’t Scratch a newly painted
door
Nor Puddle on the kitchen
floor,
Dribble, Whiff, or Moult
your hair,
On any hire-purchase Chair,
And if you have to Burp
or Sneeze
Then first jump off the owner’s
knees,
And remember – cats who Stray
DESERVE the RSPCA.’

In younger days, just for a lark,
Prudie taught herself to bark.
She kept herself amused for hours
Burying bones beneath the flowers.
But she was told, the more she grew,
This wasn't quite the thing to do.
When she asked why, they told her flat:
'Well, you're a Cat and That is That.
You should be seen but never heard.'

From then on, Prudie only purred.

And life continued quite humdrum
Until the age of thirty-one (cat years, that is)
When Prudie Pratt, our average cat,
Found out that perhaps . . .
just maybe . . .
even for her . . .
life held more than that.

And this she found out apropos
A slip-up by the GPO,
When through her door (the wrong address)
Came 'Feline Liberation Press'
('For Cats who want to Fight and Get
Away from being just a Pet').

Her first thought was, I'm loath to say,
To bung it in her litter tray.

Well, all the magazines
she'd known
Were *Pussy's Realm*
and
Pussy's Own

Which taught you
everything you'd wish
To know about when serving fish,
What to say and how to think,
And if your tail should have a kink
Then how to make it straight and true.

But this was something really new
And came as quite a shock to Prue.

PUSSY'S OWN
HOW TO KEEP THAT KITTEN LOOK
IS YOUR FUR DULL AND LIFELESS

This was written by and for
Cats in search of something more
Than PETTING (let's face it,
That's all she was getting).

Cats across the world had sent,
From Abu Dhabi, Delhi, Kent,
In news and views of how they'd fought
And how with other cats' support
Had learnt to fulfil their ambitions.

Arty Cats held Exhibitions,
Student Cats became Cat Tutors,
Some learnt how to use Computers.
Sporty Cats had had a Whack
At swimming to Calais and back

And there were Cat Explorers who
Had made the Trail to Katmandhu.

NIGHT
CATS BITE BACK
COMPUTERS
KATMANDHU
IN SEARCH OF THE CATRIARCHY
A CATS RIGHT TO CHOOSE
feline Review Conference
CATS AGAINST THE VET

Here Prudie felt a pang inside
I think a burst of Feline Pride.
These cats had done great things and yet
They'd all been brought up as a pet.
Then maybe,
maybe not,
maybe?
If They could do it SO COULD SHE!

Then with her head between her paws
Thought 'I'm too old to fight a cause,'

And with her feet behind her ears
Surveyed the boredom of her years,

And with her tail tucked 'neath her jaw
Thought 'Life can't offer me much more,'

Until in one untidy bunch
Could hardly think
as far as
lunch . . .

. . . which would have led to some distress
Had she not noticed this address:

To Cat Tabby,
'House for Sale',
Peckham High Street.
(First Class Mail).

She knew the street, she knew the place,
Her mind again began to race
And formed this Simple Plan, which was
To take it round as soon as poss.*

*Not a Herculean labour
For a next-to-next-door neighbour.

PRUDIE FINDS OUT SOME MORE

Part 2 Prudie Finds Out Some More

'House for Sale' was up for sale
Apparently to no avail –
The major reason being that
It definitely reeked of cat.
For when the owners long ago
Had moved to property in Bow
Their pet, a tabby cat, had stayed
And with some local cats had made
It into a sort of Cat HQ
Where pets and strays (their kittens too)
Could drop by . . .
                    and learn a thing or two.

HOUSE
FOR SALE
01-46835

GRR-NICA

One cat came each day at Three
To practise Judo and Tai-Chi,
And organised the weekly session
On how to cope with dog aggression.
Another cat, from foreign parts,
Experimented in The Arts
And showed that cats could never fail
In painting if they used their tail
(Proclaiming as she splodged and swished:
'I TOO am an Expressionist!')
And on the stairs the very first
All-Cat Samba Band rehearsed.

While more were bustling about,
Coming in and going out,
Climbing over odds and ends,
Bumping into Friends of Friends,
Finding that at every turn
There was something new to learn
And grabbing every chance they got
To do what average cats DO NOT.

(And though there were an awful lot
They shared out every sunny spot.)

ENTER PRUDIE on the scene,
Clinging to her magazine.

Now Prudie Pratt was seldom used
To being widely introduced
Which may be why
she quickly pranced
Behind a row of potted plants,

To look about as best she might
While keeping both her eyes shut tight!

. . . UNTIL she heard this throttled 'grrr'
From something very close to her.

And peering out in disbelief,
Through a large and jagged leaf,
She saw a kitten scrunch its face
Into the nastiest grimace
And try like anything to BARK!

How could Prudie not remark?
How could she not leap up and cry:
'Go on, have another try!
I'll show you how.'

She did. And found
Other cats had gathered round,
Not to laugh or scratch or spit,
They came to have a go at it.

From then on she had lots of fun
Making friends with everyone,
Sharing all their hopes and fears,
Helpful hints and good ideas,*
Learning things she'd never thought
Pets could POSSIBLY be taught

And doing things she'd never dare
Were any Human Beings there.

*The tabby got her paper back,
She put it on the paper rack
(for others to read).

The hours passed, the minutes flew,
It seemed no time at all to Prue.
She thought of going back – but then
How COULD she be a pet again?
How could she go back home and hide
All this new-found feline pride?
These cats, you see, had proved to her
She wasn't just a lump of fur
To be prodded, pushed and poked,
Lifted up and down and stroked.

(Besides – she had a lurking doubt
THEY'D more than likely locked her out.)

Prudie paused, she sighed, then groaned
And said: 'I DON'T WANT TO BE OWNED!
I'm going to learn to use my paws,
My whiskers, eyes and ears and claws
And (just a little) native wit
To live MY life as I SEE FIT.
That is . . . if you will help me to?'

They cheered so loud a neighbour threw
A boot at them and shouted: 'Skat!
Clearorf! Gerrout! Yer mangey cat!'

I hate to say . . .

. . . they threw it back.

The window pane still bears the crack,

In proof that cats now aim to be
Treated with EQUALITY.*

*(Though, incidentally, it would
also prove their aim is good!)

Epilogue

Prudie stayed in 'House for Sale'
What happened is another tale.

I'll say this though – the rumours fly
That Something's Up in Peckham Rye.
Why, local people even strangers
Are reporting there've been changes;
'Something 'bout the CATS,' they say
'Not like They Were in our day!!'

EQUALITY
IT'S WHAT
CATS
WANT
BOOT BOYS
RULES
DON'T
SPURS
ROAR
PECKHAM MEWS

CATS AGAINST THE DOGS OF WAR
CATS AGAINST THE CUTS
BABY
PET
BRITISH BULLDO
N
CATS OF THE WORLD UNITE
I'VE NEVER MET A NEUTERED VET... YET